ROCK
SCHOOL

GRADED SOLO EXAMS IN ROCK, JAZZ & POP

**THE OFFICIAL PUBLICATION FOR THE ROCK SCHOOL LTD
AND TRINITY COLLEGE LONDON EXAMINATIONS**

ELECTRIC GUITAR GRADE 1

EDITED BY NORTON YORK

FABER *ff* MUSIC

Trinity College
London

Preface

Welcome to Rock School Grade 1. These pieces and exercises are all about your musicianship, enthusiasm and skill. We hope you will develop your abilities as a performer and general musician by learning to play the music in Grade 1 – so that when you write and perform, in whatever style, you will have a solid background of knowledge and experience. Taking the Grade 1 exam is your opportunity to find out how well you can perform, as well as giving you the chance of an internationally recognised qualification.

NORTON YORK
Chairman, Rock School Ltd

CONTENTS

 Rock School Ltd would like to acknowledge the contribution of London's Guitar Institute, Basstech and Drumtech to the development of the Rock School grade exams

Introduction

What is a grade exam?

Grades are a system of progressive music examinations. These new grade exams for electric guitar, bass and drums are the result of a collaboration between Rock School Ltd, and Trinity College London. The exams are validated by Trinity College and have the same status as all other Trinity grade exams. Trinity College first offered grades in classical music over 100 years ago and they are now taken by hundreds of thousands of students worldwide.

The Rock School/Trinity grade exams are recognised by many A-level and other examination boards as part of their assessment process, including the Oxford Delegacy of Local Examinations, the University of London, the Welsh Joint Education Committee, the Oxford and Cambridge Schools Examination Board and the University of Cambridge Local Examinations Syndicate. They are also approved by the Education and Training Committee of the Musicians Union.

Who's who

This exam syllabus has been devised and written by some of the UK's leading educators and instrument instructors to make it relevant to you as you develop your talent and skill as a performer.

Norton York (General Editor and chairman of the examiners panel).

Norton is Development Director of Commercial Music at the University of Westminster. His publications include: *The Rock File: Making it in the Music Business* (OUP 1991) and *Pop Goes to College* (WIRED 1992). He is also chairman of Rock School Ltd.

PRINCIPAL EXAMINERS:

Rob Burns *(bass)*

Rob is one of the UK's leading session bass players and clinicians. He has performed with Pete Townshend, Dave Gilmour and Jerry Donahue, while also working as an active film and video composer. He is Head of Department at London's premier Basstech school and the musical director of the Musicians Union's MUzictech demonstration band. Rob is a regular contributor to *Guitarist*.

Alan Limbrick *(guitar)*

Alan is the founder director of London's Guitar Institute and Basstech. After studying at GIT in Hollywood, Alan performed and recorded with Art of Noise, David Knopfler, and Joan Armatrading before launching the Guitar Institute in 1986. Alan is the writer of the 'Blues' column in *Guitarist*.

Francis Seriau *(drums)*

Francis is the founder director of the Drumtech percussion school in West London. He has pioneered modern approaches to learning the kit as well as latin percussion.

He has taught many of the leading drummers in the UK, including Bill Bruford (King Crimson and the Bill Bruford Band) and Rat Scabies (The Damned). Francis has a regular latin column in *Rhythm*.

What is in a Grade 1 exam?

You will be required to perform one of the two groups of performance pieces published in this book. There will also be simple exercises on instrument technique, and sight-reading tests. Finally, there are ear tests and general musicianship questions. These are all explained below.

The exams are marked out of 100. To pass a grade exam you need to score 65 or better (it is not necessary to pass each section). A pass mark with merit starts at 75 and a pass with distinction is at 85 or above. Each year, professional equipment will be awarded by Rock School Ltd for the best Grade exam performance on each instrument.

MARKING STRUCTURE AT A GLANCE:

	Maximum	Pass
Performance piece 1	20	13
Performance piece 2	20	13
Performance piece 3	20	13
Technical exercises	15	11
Sight-reading	10	6
Ear tests	10	6
General musicianship	5	3
TOTAL	100	65

Performance pieces

There are six performance pieces in this grade, divided into two groups of three each. You will be required to play all three pieces in **either** Group A **or** Group B. The notation guide on page 5 is designed to help you learn the pieces. In the exam you **must** perform your chosen pieces to a 'music minus 1' style cassette (see the cassette order form).

GROUP A	GROUP B
Time to Think	Cultural Attitude
Hard Shoulder to Cry On	Twang Thang
Won't Techno for an Answer	If Three were Four

Total marks available for each performance piece: 20. Pass mark:13

Technical exercises

The exercises are in three groups, and you should practice them all. The examiner will ask you to play **one** exercise from each group. Where applicable, these exercises should be played at the speeds given to you by the examiner, which will be within the range of speeds marked by each exercise.

Total marks available: 15. Pass mark: 11

Sight-reading

The examiner will give you a sight-reading test, and will allow you up to 1½ minutes to prepare. You will be given the speed for the test by the examiner. There are four sample sight-reading tests in this book, to show you the level of difficulty to expect in the Grade 1 exam. These sight-reading tests **will not** be used in the Grade 1 exam itself.

Total marks available: 10. Pass mark: 6

Ear tests

In the exam you will be asked to perform a number of ear tests involving pitch, rhythm and chords. Each ear test will be played to you twice on a cassette. You will be expected to give your answer after hearing each test for the second time. The ear tests in this book are samples and **will not** be used in the exam.

Total marks available: 10. Pass mark: 6

General musicianship

At the end of the exam, the examiner will ask you up to four general musicianship questions. The majority of these concern the music you have played in the performance pieces. The topics covered are given in this book along with sample questions and answers.

Total marks available: 5. Pass mark: 3

Exam procedure

The Grade 1 exam will last up to 15 minutes. You should arrive at the exam centre at least 15 minutes prior to the exam so that you can register and get ready to play. There will be a waiting room for you to prepare yourself. You will be taken to the exam room by a representative of Rock School Ltd. The examiner will welcome you into the room and give you a little time to set up your instrument. After meeting the examiner, the first thing you should do is to check the equipment. This should be done as quickly as possible. The examiner will give you a choice at the start. You may either play the technical exercises first or the performance pieces. Depending on your decision, these are the two possible orders of events in the exam:

ORDER ONE	ORDER TWO
Performance piece 1	Technical exercises
Performance piece 2	Performance piece 1
Performance piece 3	Performance piece 2
Technical exercises	Performance piece 3
Sight-reading	Sight-reading
Ear tests	Ear tests
General musicianship	General musicianship

After the exam, your result, with a mark sheet, will be confirmed by post usually within 14 days. The mark sheet shows your score in each section, your score overall, and the examiner's comments. If you have passed Grade 1, your RSL-Trinity College London grade certificate will also be included.

On submitting the exam entry form, each candidate is issued with a personal entry number, which is also printed on your cassette. The cassette is part of the exam and should be kept safely. **You must bring your personal grade cassette with you to the exam**, and its number will be logged at the exam centre by a representative of Rock School Ltd. Rock School Ltd reserves the right to refuse access to the examination room to any candidate whose personal entry and cassette numbers do not match.

Exam centres and the equipment you will need

There is a network of exam centres around the country where you can take your grade exam. Exam centres are located in existing music schools, in recording or rehearsal studios, or in music shops. Full details of all current exam centres are available direct from Rock School Ltd (address on exam entry form). Each centre is fitted with most of the equipment you need to take the exam. However, you should bring your own guitar and leads. At each exam centre there will be a waiting room and a separate room for you to prepare for your exam.

Notation Guide

The notation and dynamics used in the band pieces, solo studies, and exercises generally follow conventional musical notation. Tablature is also printed for the band pieces and the solo studies for electric guitar in Grades 3 and 5, and bass guitar in Grade 3. *Note*: this notation guide applies to all Rock School graded material for electric guitar, bass guitar and drums, and may contain references not specifically used in this pack.

General notation

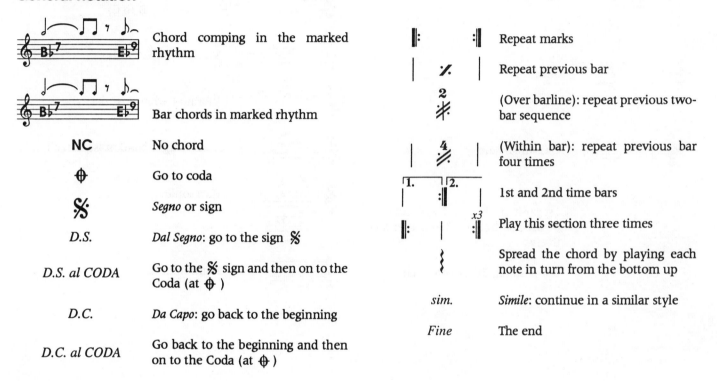

	Chord comping in the marked rhythm		Repeat marks
	Bar chords in marked rhythm	*%*	Repeat previous bar
NC	No chord	**2** /	(Over barline): repeat previous two-bar sequence
⊕	Go to coda	**4** /	(Within bar): repeat previous bar four times
𝄋	*Segno* or sign	1. 2.	1st and 2nd time bars
D.S.	*Dal Segno*: go to the sign 𝄋	x3	Play this section three times
D.S. al CODA	Go to the 𝄋 sign and then on to the Coda (at ⊕)		Spread the chord by playing each note in turn from the bottom up
D.C.	*Da Capo*: go back to the beginning	*sim.*	*Simile*: continue in a similar style
D.C. al CODA	Go back to the beginning and then on to the Coda (at ⊕)	*Fine*	The end

Dynamics and accents

>	Accent	*mp*	*Mezzo piano*: moderately soft
∧	Heavy accent	*mf*	*Mezzo forte*: moderately loud
–	*Tenuto*: slight accent	*f*	*Forte*: loud
♩ or ♪	*Staccato*: play short and sharp	*ff*	*Fortissimo*: very loud
pp	*Pianissimo*: very soft	< or *cresc.*	*Crescendo*: getting louder
p	*Piano*: soft	> or *dim.*	*Diminuendo*: getting softer

Electric guitar

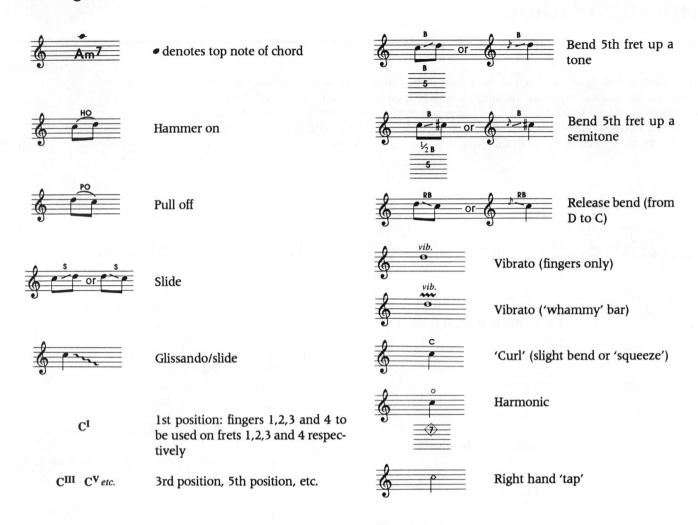

denotes top note of chord

Hammer on

Pull off

Slide

Glissando/slide

C^I   1st position: fingers 1,2,3 and 4 to be used on frets 1,2,3 and 4 respectively

C^{III} C^V *etc.*   3rd position, 5th position, etc.

Bend 5th fret up a tone

Bend 5th fret up a semitone

Release bend (from D to C)

Vibrato (fingers only)

Vibrato ('whammy' bar)

'Curl' (slight bend or 'squeeze')

Harmonic

Right hand 'tap'

Time to Think

Dave Barnard

Hard Shoulder to Cry On

Lee Hodgson

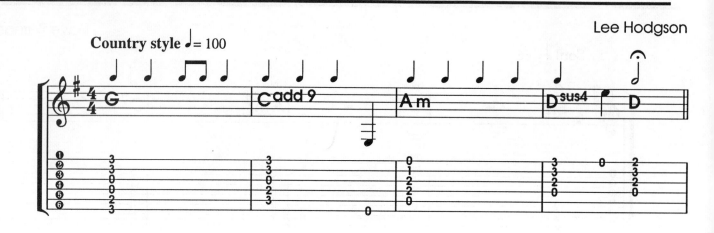

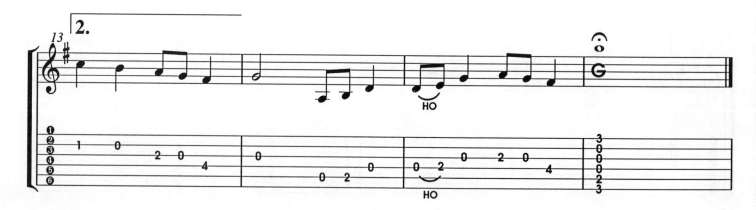

Entry Form

ROCK SCHOOL GRADE EXAMS

Use this form if you wish to enter yourself for a Rock School grade exam. Please ensure that you have read the Exam Regulations before filling in this form. This entry form and your cheque or postal order (made payable to **Rock School Ltd**) should be sent to: Exam Entries, Rock School Ltd, Broomfield House, Broomfield Road, Richmond, Surrey TW9 3HS. Telephone: (0181) 332 6303. Please enclose two 1st class stamps and a stamped self-addressed postcard with this completed form.

1995/6 Exam Entry Fees
(per candidate)

	Grade 1	Grade 3	Grade 5	Grade 6	Grade 8
1995	£ 16.00	£ 18.00	£ 24.00	£ 30.00	£ 36.00
1996-8	£ 18.00	£ 20.00	£ 26.00	£ 32.00	£ 38.00

Full name   _____

Address   _____

_____

Post Code   _____

Telephone   _____

Cassette Registration No.   _____
(if cassette already purchased)

Grade (please tick)

1	3	5	6	8

Instrument (please tick)

Guitar	Bass	Drums

Exam Period / Year

(please tick – see 'Exam Regulations' for details)

A	B	C	D	E	F

1995	1996	1997

Amount enclosed (please tick)

1995	£ 16.00	£ 18.00	£ 24.00	£ 30.00	£ 36.00
1996-8	£ 18.00	£ 20.00	£ 26.00	£ 32.00	£ 38.00

Teacher's Entry Form

ROCK SCHOOL GRADE EXAMS

Use this form if you wish to enter one or more pupils for Rock School grade exams. Please ensure that you have read the Exam Regulations before filling in this form. This entry form and your cheque or postal order (made payable to **Rock School Ltd**) should be sent to: Exam Entries, Rock School Ltd, Broomfield House, Broomfield Road, Richmond, Surrey TW9 3HS. Telephone: (0181) 332 6303. Please enclose two 1st class stamps and a stamped self-addressed postcard with this completed form.

1995 Exam Entry Fees
(per candidate)

	Grade 1	Grade 3	Grade 5	Grade 6	Grade 8
1995	£ 16.00	£ 18.00	£ 24.00	£ 30.00	£ 36.00
1996-8	£ 18.00	£ 20.00	£ 26.00	£ 32.00	£ 38.00

Teacher's full name _____

Address _____

_____

Post Code _____

Telephone _____

CANDIDATE'S FULL NAME	GRADE	INSTRUMENT	EXAM PERIOD * (PERIOD / YEAR)	CASSETTE REGISTRATION NUMBER **	FEE

* See 'Exam Regulations' for details.
** Fill in this information if candidate has already purchased a cassette.

Total amount enclosed: £ _____

Cassette Order Form

ROCK SCHOOL GRADE EXAMS

In order to enter a Rock School grade exam each candidate must have the correct Rock School cassette for his/her instrument and grade. This is used during the examination as backing for the band pieces, and is also designed to assist practice when preparing for the exam.

Each cassette will be stamped with the candidate's own personal registration number and will be checked when he/she arrives at the exam centre. **Each candidate must bring his/her personal grade cassette to the exam.** Lost cassettes will only be replaced at full cost price. Rock School Ltd reserves the right to refuse access to the examination room to any candidate who attempts to take an exam with an unauthorised cassette, or whose personal entry and cassette registration numbers do not match.

Rock School Cassettes (per grade/instrument)
Price: £7.20 (including VAT, postage and packing)

Full name _____

CANDIDATE / TEACHER (delete as applicable)

Address _____

_____

Post Code _____

Telephone _____

CANDIDATE'S FULL NAME	PERSONAL EXAM ENTRY NUMBER (if known)	GRADE	INSTRUMENT

Total number of cassettes ordered:	
Total amount enclosed (£7.20 per cassette):	£

This cassette order form and your cheque or postal order (made payable to Rock School Ltd) should be sent to: Exam Entries, Rock School Ltd, Broomfield House, Broomfield Road, Richmond, Surrey TW9 3HS. Telephone: (0181) 332 6303.

Exam regulations

Candidates are advised to read these regulations carefully.

1. Rock School grade exams are open to all persons, irrespective of age.

2. Candidates will be examined according to the requirements of the Rock School grade exams syllabus only. Both candidates and teachers should make sure they are thoroughly familiar with the Rock School syllabus and exam regulations as published in this book.

3. Candidates wishing to enter for a Rock School grade exam should fill in the appropriate form and return it, with the correct fee, to: Exam Entries, Rock School Ltd, Broomfield House, Broomfield Road, Richmond, Surrey, TW9 3HS. Telephone: (0181) 332 6303. Teachers wishing to enter pupils should fill in the teacher's entry form.

4. Candidates may not transfer their exams from one centre to another. Any candidate wishing to postpone an exam must re-apply and pay the appropriate fees.

5. Exam entries may not be transferred from one candidate to another.

6. Candidates will only be permitted to take a Rock School grade exam if they have paid the correct fee in advance. Exam fees will not be refunded.

7. Any candidate unable to attend an exam because of illness may apply to Rock School Ltd for a half-fee re-entry permit at the same centre, enclosing a medical certificate and the original appointment slip. No such half-fee re-entry applications will be allowed if more than 30 days have elapsed from the date of the original exam.

8. Although all exam material should be prepared in full, the examiner may not necessarily require a complete performance of each prepared piece.

9. Candidates must use only the correct published grade music in the examination. **Photocopying of any of the material contained within the official published pack is prohibited**.

10. Candidates must use the correct Rock School cassette for their instrument/grade in the exam. The candidate's personal entry and cassette registration numbers must match.

11. No-one other than the examiner and the candidate will be allowed to attend the exam, with the exception of moderators appointed jointly by Rock School Ltd and Trinity College London.

12. The examiner's decision is final. The examiner may stop an examination when a decision has been reached.

13. Rock School Ltd reserves the right to refuse any candidate who fails to comply with these regulations.

Examination periods

Rock School operates six exam periods per year. Completed exam entry forms with the correct payment must reach Rock School Ltd at the address on the entry form not later than the closing date for the candidate's chosen exam period.

1995

PERIOD	FROM	TO	CLOSING DATE
A	2 January	10 February	17 Dec (94)
B	13 February	31 March	27 January
C	10 April	26 May	24 March
D	29 May	7 July	12 May
E	11 September	20 October	26 August
F	23 October	8 December	6 October

1996

PERIOD	FROM	TO	CLOSING DATE
A	15 January	9 February	1 Nov (95)
B	26 February	30 March	10 January
C	23 April	25 May	1 March
D	11 June	6 July	1 May
E	25 September	19 October	1 July
F	12 November	14 December	1 October

1997

PERIOD	FROM	TO	CLOSING DATE
A	14 January	8 February	1 Dec (96)
B	25 February	29 March	10 January
C	22 April	23 May	1 March
D	9 Jun	5 July	1 May
E	24 September	18 October	1 July
F	11 November	13 December	1 October

Won't Techno for an Answer

Adrian York

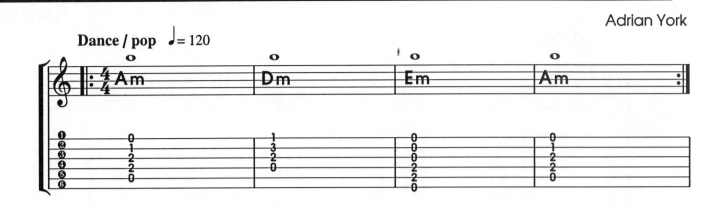

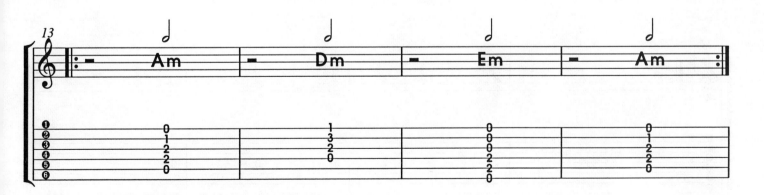

Cultural Attitude

Adrian York

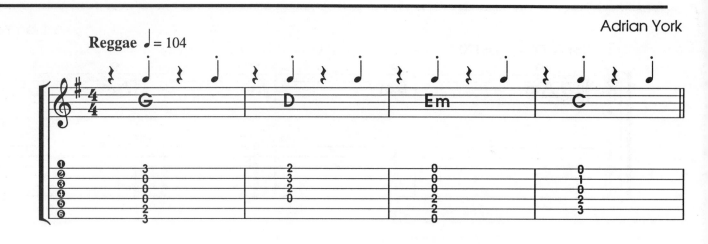

Twang Thang

Alan Limbrick

If Three were Four

Deirdre Cartwright

Technical exercises

The tempo for each exercise in Groups A and B is ♩ = 90. You will be given this pulse in your exam, and the exercises must be played in quarter notes/crotchets. In Group C, the exercises must be played promptly.

All scales must be played up and down; start on the lowest note, play the highest note once, and finish on the lowest note.

Group A: scales

1. G major pentatonic.

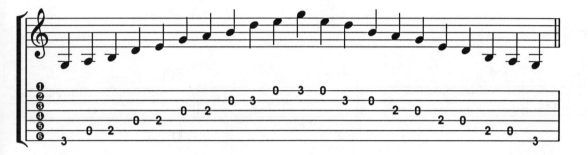

2. G major.

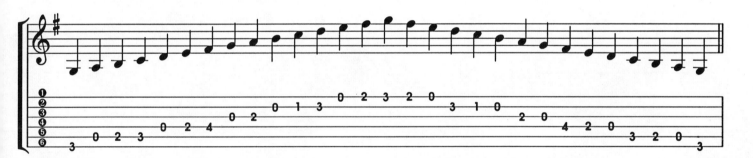

3. E minor blues scale.

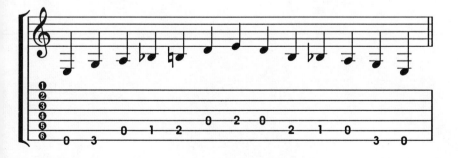

Group B: chords

E major   A Major   D major

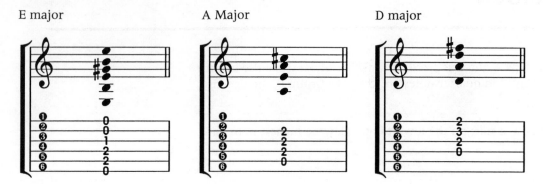

Group C: intervals in G major

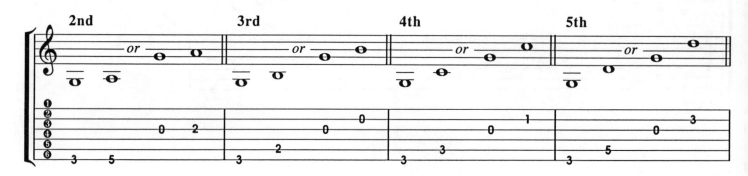

Sight-reading

Sample 1

Sample 2

Sample 3

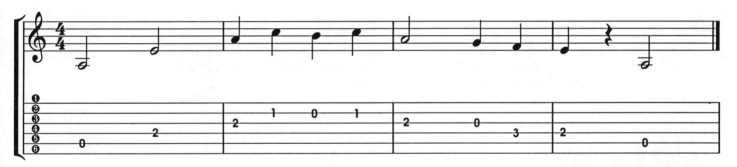

Sample 4

Ear tests

TEST 1

To clap the rhythm of a melody of no more than two bars in 4/4 time after hearing it twice (3 marks). Tempo range: ♩ = 60-80.

Sample

TEST 2

To hear the tonic note of a major chord, and to identify two notes within the first octave of that major chord, giving either their degrees of the major scale or their tonic solfa names (3 marks).

Sample

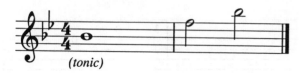

(tonic)

Answer: 5th and octave of the major scale, or so and doh.

TEST 3

To hear and identify two chords in a major key taken from the following (in root position): I, IV, V, V7, II minor, (e.g. in C major C, F, G, G7, Dm). The tonic triad and name of the key will be given to the candidate (4 marks). Tempo range: ♩ = 60-80.

Sample

(tonic triad)

Answer: chords IV and II minor, or A major and F♯ minor.

General musicianship

TOPICS

1. The pitch, duration and relative value of notes and rests.
2. Time signatures and marks of expression.
3. Simple questions on guitar construction.

Sample questions and answers

These are the type of questions the examiner will ask you at the end of the exam. The questions about musical notation will refer to the performance pieces you have played.

Q   What kind of note is this: ♩ ?
A   *A crotchet or quarter note.*

Q   What kind of rest is this: ♪ ?
A   *A quaver or eighth note rest.*

Q   What does this time signature mean: $\frac{4}{4}$?
A   *Four crotchet (quarter note) beats in every bar.*

Q   What does *cresc.* mean?
A   *It means 'crescendo', increasing in volume.*

Q   What are 'machine heads' used for?
A   *Machine head is another term for tuning peg, used to tune the guitar's strings.*

Q   What do the electric guitar's main control knobs do?
A   *They alter the volume and tone of the signal and select different pick-up combinations.*